The Graphic Novel

Sleeping Beauty

RETOLD BY **MARTIN POWELL**

ILLUSTRATED BY
SEAN DIETRICH

Raintree

www.raintreepublishers.co.uk
Visit our website to find out
more information about
Raintree books.

To order:
☎ Phone 0845 6044371
🖹 Fax +44 (0) 1865 312263
✉ Email myorders@raintreepublishers.co.uk

Customers from outside the UK please telephone +44 1865 312262

Raintree is an imprint of Capstone Global Library Limited, a company incorporated in
England and Wales having its registered office at 7 Pilgrim Street, London EC4V 6LB
Registered company number: 6695882

Text © Stone Arch Books 2009
First published by Stone Arch Books in 2009
First published in paperback in the United Kingdom by Capstone Global Library in 2013
The moral rights of the proprietor have been asserted.

Editor: Laura Knowles
Art Director: Heather Kindseth
Graphic Designer: Brann Garvey
Printed and bound in China by CTPS

ISBN 978 1 406 24771 8 (paperback)
16 15 14 13 12
10 9 8 7 6 5 4 3 2 1

British Library Cataloguing in Publication Data
Powell, Martin, 1959-
Sleeping Beauty. -- (Graphic spin)
741.5-dc23
A full catalogue record for this book is available from the British Library.

Cast of Characters

KING

QUEEN

THIRTEENTH FAIRY

PRINCE

ROSE
THE SLEEPING BEAUTY

Once upon a time in a Welsh kingdom, there lived a king and queen.

They were kind, noble rulers loved by all of their subjects.

Their days were healthy and rich, filled with everything almost anyone could ever desire.

Yet they felt a great emptiness. Something was missing.

And without it, they could never be truly happy.

Twelve months later, the words of the wise old creature came true.

A beautiful, perfect princess was born to the queen and king.

A feast was prepared in celebration, and all the magical folk in the kingdom were invited.

Plates of the purest gold were set upon the great table awaiting the twelve Good Fairies.

The Fairies were ageless sisters of great power.

Each one of them had a magical gift.

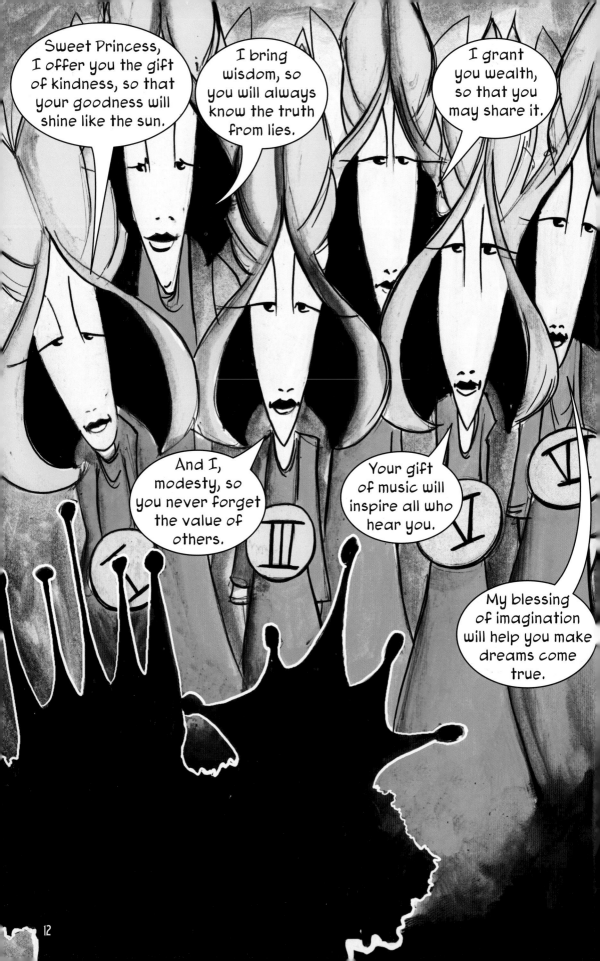

The Good Fairies' gifts made Princess Rose wise, kind, and beautiful. She was loved by all who met her.

As the years flew by, the king and queen forgot about the evil curse.

Early one morning they set out to find a birthday gift for the princess, leaving Rose alone in the palace.

It was her fifteenth birthday.

Princess Rose would sleep for one hundred years.

Heartbroken, the king and queen were overcome by the same dark sleep.

The curse had started to spread.

Soon, the entire castle fell into an awful slumber . . .

. . . followed by the entire kingdom.

"It feels like I've seen you before."

Princess Rose, I know your face. I know you.

It's just like . . .

Magic.

Suddenly . . .

You fool . . .

None may save the Sleeping Beauty.

The Thirteenth Fairy's evil spell had brought the fallen knights back to life.

Yes.

It's a dream come true.

The curse had been lifted.

Soon, life returned to the slumbering kingdom.

Upon their return, the king and queen found that their forgotten fears had come true.

The curse had been fulfilled.

And there was nothing they could do to stop it.

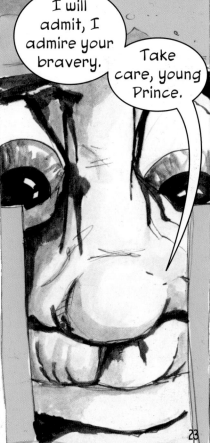

23

As the prince slashed through the deadly thorns, he felt as though he was not alone.

Suddenly, evil eyes blinked open all around him.

Who goes there?!

SSKKRREEEE

SSKKRREEEE

FWOOSH

Just a few pesky bats.

Be gone, all of you!

As the bats scattered, the prince saw something truly frightening.

He had found what was left of the knights who had gone before him.

Rest in peace, fallen knight.

CREAK

I will finish the quest that you began.

Soon, the prince came upon the sleeping rulers.

So the legend is true.

The spell of sleep still holds.

The scent of roses is much stronger near the tower.

That's where I'll find her.

CRASHH!!

Princess Rose . . .

The prince was not afraid.

SMACK!

He quickly defeated the first skeleton.

But as he turned to fight the others . . .

SWOOSH!

THWAP!!

. . . a mighty blow sent him flying through the window.

Ugh!

POP!

After one hundred years of slumber, the Sleeping Beauty's dreams had finally come true.

She found her prince.

And they lived happily together, ever after.

ABOUT THE AUTHOR

Since 1986, Martin Powell has been a freelance writer. He has written hundreds of stories, many of which have been published by Disney, Marvel, Tekno Comix, Moonstone Books, and others. In 1989, Powell received an Eisner Award nomination for his graphic novel *Scarlet in Gaslight.* This award is one of the highest comic book honours.

ABOUT THE ILLUSTRATOR

Sean Dietrich has been drawing since the age of 4. He had his first art show at age 6, self-published his first comic book at 16, and has won more than 53 art awards throughout the years. When he's not drawing, Dietrich says he spends too much time in front of the TV playing video games.

OTHER BOOKS IN THE SERIES

Beauty and the Beast   978 1 406 24317 8

Jack and the Beanstalk   978 1 406 24319 2

Red Riding Hood   978 1 406 24772 5

MORE FAIRY TALES TO ENJOY

The book may be over, but the adventure is just beginning. There are many other exciting and fantastical tales for you to discover:

Grimm's Fairy Tales (Usborne Illustrated), Ruth Brocklehurst
    (Usborne, 2010)
Hans Christian Andersen's Fairy Tales (Usborne Illustrated),
    (Usborne, 2011)

WRITING PROMPTS

1. Fairy tales are fantasy stories, often about wizards, goblins, giants, and fairies. Many fairy tales have a happy ending. Write your own fairy tale. Then read it to a friend or family member.

2. Write a new version of "Sleeping Beauty" with a different curse. Maybe Sleeping Beauty becomes Dancing Beauty, a girl who cannot stop dancing for 10 years. What curse can you think up?

3. Imagine that someone else woke Sleeping Beauty before the prince had a chance. What if an old woman woke her up by vacuuming? Or perhaps a little boy tickled her with a feather. Write the wake-up scene between this new character and Sleeping Beauty.

Discussion questions

1. Pretend you are one of the fairies who grants a gift to the baby princess. What gift would you give the princess and why?

2. Imagine everyone in your school fell asleep for a hundred years, just like the kingdom in the story. How would life be different when you all woke up?

3. Fairy tales are often told over and over again. Have you heard the "Sleeping Beauty" fairy tale before? How is this version of the story different from other versions you've heard, seen, or read?

Over the years, there have been many variations of the classic fairy tale, and the "sleeping beauty" herself has been given different names by different authors.

Sleeping Beauty is the theme of a famous Russian ballet composed by Pyotr Tchaikovsky in 1890. Tchaikovsky's music was also used in the Walt Disney film version of the fairy tale. The 1959 film took five years to animate. It cost $6 million dollars to make, but the film earned only $3 million when it hit cinemas. Today, however, *Sleeping Beauty* is considered one of Disney's classics. It is the Disney version of the story that many people are most familiar with.

Glossary

ageless seeming never to grow old

curse evil spell intended to harm someone

graciousness people who are gracious do what is polite, kind, and right

desire strong wish or need for something or someone

legend story handed down from earlier times

modesty people who are modest do not brag about their abilities or possessions

spindle rod on a spinning wheel that holds or winds thread

stubborn not willing to change

superstitious believing that some things are lucky or unlucky

virtue good quality or characteristic

THE HISTORY OF
SLEEPING BEAUTY

Like so many fairy tales, the story of Sleeping Beauty was first an oral tale. It was passed from person to person though speech, rather than being written down. In 1697, a French author, Charles Perrault, published a written collection of these fairy tales. His book included "Little Red Riding Hood", "Cinderella", and of course, "The Sleeping Beauty in the Wood".

Perrault's story included a second part, which takes place after the prince wakes Sleeping Beauty. The happy pair are married and have two children. But the prince keeps his marriage a secret from his mother, who is an ogress (female ogre). After he takes the throne, the prince brings his family to the castle. When he is called away to war, his monster mother makes plans to eat her daughter-in-law and grandchildren. The prince returns just in time. His mother throws herself in a pit of snakes, and the rest of the family is free to live happily ever after.